TATE DIARY
2022

TATE GENERAL INFORMATION

Tate is a family of four galleries: Tate Britain and Tate Modern in London, Tate Liverpool and Tate St Ives. Each features a particular area of the Tate collection. Tate Britain shows British art from 1500 to the present day, including the Turner Bequest. Tate Modern displays international modern art from 1900 to the present day. Tate Liverpool shows selections of modern and international contemporary art, while Tate St Ives displays works by the St Ives School in the context in which they were created, as well as international modern and contemporary art.

The collection consists of painting, sculpture, installation works and large numbers of watercolours, drawings and modern prints. Artists in the collection include Hogarth, Turner, Constable, Rossetti, Matisse, Picasso, Giacometti, Hepworth, Rothko, Dalí, Bacon, Pollock, Warhol, Riley, Hockney, Hirst and many others.

EVENTS
All four galleries offer a full programme of talks, courses, films and events for adults, young people and families relating to the collection and to exhibitions and displays.

INFORMATION
Visit www.tate.org.uk for details of exhibitions, displays and events. For information on Tate Britain and Tate Modern call 020 7887 8888; on Tate Liverpool, 0151 702 7400; and on Tate St Ives, 01736 796226.

DISABLED VISITORS
Tate welcomes people with disabilities. A number of wheelchairs are available at each gallery and there is lift access in all four galleries. If you would like further information, call the appropriate number given above.

TATE PUBLISHING
A books catalogue is available on request from Tate Enterprises, Millbank, London SW1P 4RG, or by telephoning 020 7887 8869. For more information on our titles visit www.tate.org.uk/publishing.

TATE SHOPS
Tate Shops offer a wide range of books, posters, cards and merchandise related to Tate, the collection and exhibitions. For online purchases visit www.shop.tate.org.uk.

TATE CAFÉS AND RESTAURANTS
All four galleries offer an excellent choice of light meals, snacks and drinks. Tate Britain's Rex Whistler restaurant has an à la carte menu, a set daily menu and a fine wine list.
For reservations call 020 7887 8825 and for the Tate Modern restaurant call 020 7887 8888.

TATE MEMBERS
Support Tate and become a Member to enjoy:
- Unlimited free entry to all Tate exhibitions
- Exclusive access to Members Rooms at Tate Britain and Tate Modern
- Regular listings guides and TATE ETC magazine to your door
- Special viewing opportunities and fast-track exhibition entry

Your support will help acquire works of art for the collection and provide vital funding for Tate's exciting programme, so you'll be shaping the Tate of the future.

Join in the gallery, online at tate.org.uk/members, call 020 7887 8888 or email members@tate.org.uk

2022 PUBLIC HOLIDAYS

UNITED KINGDOM	
New Year's Day (substitute day)	3 January
St Patrick's Day (N.I. only)	17 March
Good Friday	15 April
Easter Monday	18 April
Early May Bank Holiday	2 May
Spring Bank Holiday	2 June
Platinum Jubilee Bank Holiday	3 June
Public Holiday (N.I. only)	12 July
Summer Bank Holiday (Scotland only)	1 August
Summer Bank Holiday	29 August
Boxing Day	26 December
Christmas Day (substitute day)	27 December

2022

JANUARY
Monday		3	10	17	24	31
Tuesday		4	11	18	25	
Wednesday		5	12	19	26	
Thursday		6	13	20	27	
Friday		7	14	21	28	
Saturday	1	8	15	22	29	
Sunday	2	9	16	23	30	

FEBRUARY
Monday		7	14	21	28
Tuesday	1	8	15	22	
Wednesday	2	9	16	23	
Thursday	3	10	17	24	
Friday	4	11	18	25	
Saturday	5	12	19	26	
Sunday	6	13	20	27	

MARCH
Monday		7	14	21	28	
Tuesday	1	8	15	22	29	
Wednesday	2	9	16	23	30	
Thursday	3	10	17	24	31	
Friday	4	11	18	25		
Saturday	5	12	19	26		
Sunday	6	13	20	27		

APRIL
Monday		4	11	18	25	
Tuesday		5	12	19	26	
Wednesday		6	13	20	27	
Thursday		7	14	21	28	
Friday	1	8	15	22	29	
Saturday	2	9	16	23	30	
Sunday	3	10	17	24		

MAY
Monday		2	9	16	23	30
Tuesday		3	10	17	24	31
Wednesday		4	11	18	25	
Thursday		5	12	19	26	
Friday		6	13	20	27	
Saturday		7	14	21	28	
Sunday	1	8	15	22	29	

JUNE
Monday		6	13	20	27	
Tuesday		7	14	21	28	
Wednesday	1	8	15	22	29	
Thursday	2	9	16	23	30	
Friday	3	10	17	24		
Saturday	4	11	18	25		
Sunday	5	12	19	26		

JULY
Monday		4	11	18	25	
Tuesday		5	12	19	26	
Wednesday		6	13	20	27	
Thursday		7	14	21	28	
Friday	1	8	15	22	29	
Saturday	2	9	16	23	30	
Sunday	3	10	17	24	31	

AUGUST
Monday	1	8	15	22	29
Tuesday	2	9	16	23	30
Wednesday	3	10	17	24	31
Thursday	4	11	18	25	
Friday	5	12	19	26	
Saturday	6	13	20	27	
Sunday	7	14	21	28	

SEPTEMBER
Monday		5	12	19	26
Tuesday		6	13	20	27
Wednesday		7	14	21	28
Thursday	1	8	15	22	29
Friday	2	9	16	23	30
Saturday	3	10	17	24	
Sunday	4	11	18	25	

OCTOBER
Monday		3	10	17	24	31
Tuesday		4	11	18	25	
Wednesday		5	12	19	26	
Thursday		6	13	20	27	
Friday		7	14	21	28	
Saturday	1	8	15	22	29	
Sunday	2	9	16	23	30	

NOVEMBER
Monday		7	14	21	28
Tuesday	1	8	15	22	29
Wednesday	2	9	16	23	30
Thursday	3	10	17	24	
Friday	4	11	18	25	
Saturday	5	12	19	26	
Sunday	6	13	20	27	

DECEMBER
Monday		5	12	19	26
Tuesday		6	13	20	27
Wednesday		7	14	21	28
Thursday	1	8	15	22	29
Friday	2	9	16	23	30
Saturday	3	10	17	24	31
Sunday	4	11	18	25	

2023

JANUARY
Monday		2	9	16	23	30
Tuesday		3	10	17	24	31
Wednesday		4	11	18	25	
Thursday		5	12	19	26	
Friday		6	13	20	27	
Saturday		7	14	21	28	
Sunday	1	8	15	22	29	

FEBRUARY
Monday		6	13	20	27
Tuesday		7	14	21	28
Wednesday	1	8	15	22	
Thursday	2	9	16	23	
Friday	3	10	17	24	
Saturday	4	11	18	25	
Sunday	5	12	19	26	

MARCH
Monday		6	13	20	27	
Tuesday		7	14	21	28	
Wednesday	1	8	15	22	29	
Thursday	2	9	16	23	30	
Friday	3	10	17	24	31	
Saturday	4	11	18	25		
Sunday	5	12	19	26		

APRIL
Monday		3	10	17	24	
Tuesday		4	11	18	25	
Wednesday		5	12	19	26	
Thursday		6	13	20	27	
Friday		7	14	21	28	
Saturday	1	8	15	22	29	
Sunday	2	9	16	23	30	

MAY
Monday	1	8	15	22	29
Tuesday	2	9	16	23	30
Wednesday	3	10	17	24	31
Thursday	4	11	18	25	
Friday	5	12	19	26	
Saturday	6	13	20	27	
Sunday	7	14	21	28	

JUNE
Monday		5	12	19	26
Tuesday		6	13	20	27
Wednesday		7	14	21	28
Thursday	1	8	15	22	29
Friday	2	9	16	23	30
Saturday	3	10	17	24	
Sunday	4	11	18	25	

JULY
Monday		3	10	17	24	31
Tuesday		4	11	18	25	
Wednesday		5	12	19	26	
Thursday		6	13	20	27	
Friday		7	14	21	28	
Saturday	1	8	15	22	29	
Sunday	2	9	16	23	30	

AUGUST
Monday		7	14	21	28
Tuesday	1	8	15	22	29
Wednesday	2	9	16	23	30
Thursday	3	10	17	24	31
Friday	4	11	18	25	
Saturday	5	12	19	26	
Sunday	6	13	20	27	

SEPTEMBER
Monday		4	11	18	25
Tuesday		5	12	19	26
Wednesday		6	13	20	27
Thursday		7	14	21	28
Friday	1	8	15	22	29
Saturday	2	9	16	23	30
Sunday	3	10	17	24	

OCTOBER
Monday		2	9	16	23	30
Tuesday		3	10	17	24	31
Wednesday		4	11	18	25	
Thursday		5	12	19	26	
Friday		6	13	20	27	
Saturday		7	14	21	28	
Sunday	1	8	15	22	29	

NOVEMBER
Monday		6	13	20	27
Tuesday		7	14	21	28
Wednesday	1	8	15	22	29
Thursday	2	9	16	23	30
Friday	3	10	17	24	
Saturday	4	11	18	25	
Sunday	5	12	19	26	

DECEMBER
Monday		4	11	18	25
Tuesday		5	12	19	26
Wednesday		6	13	20	27
Thursday		7	14	21	28
Friday	1	8	15	22	29
Saturday	2	9	16	23	30
Sunday	3	10	17	24	31

2022 YEAR PLANNER

JANUARY

Monday	Tuesday	Wednesday	Thursday	Friday	Saturday	Sunday
					1	2
3	4	5	6	7	8	9
10	11	12	13	14	15	16
17	18	19	20	21	22	23
24	25	26	27	28	29	30

JANUARY / FEBRUARY

Monday	Tuesday	Wednesday	Thursday	Friday	Saturday	Sunday
31	1	2	3	4	5	6
7	8	9	10	11	12	13
14	15	16	17	18	19	20
21	22	23	24	25	26	27
28						

MARCH

Monday	Tuesday	Wednesday	Thursday	Friday	Saturday	Sunday
	1	2	3	4	5	6
7	8	9	10	11	12	13
14	15	16	17	18	19	20
21	22	23	24	25	26	27
28	29	30	31			

APRIL

Monday	Tuesday	Wednesday	Thursday	Friday	Saturday	Sunday
				1	2	3
4	5	6	7	8	9	10
11	12	13	14	15	16	17
18	19	20	21	22	23	24
25	26	27	28	29	30	

MAY

Monday	Tuesday	Wednesday	Thursday	Friday	Saturday	Sunday
						1
2	3	4	5	6	7	8
9	10	11	12	13	14	15
16	17	18	19	20	21	22
23	24	25	26	27	28	29

MAY / JUNE

Monday	Tuesday	Wednesday	Thursday	Friday	Saturday	Sunday
30	31	1	2	3	4	5
6	7	8	9	10	11	12
13	14	15	16	17	18	19
20	21	22	23	24	25	26
27	28	29	30			

JULY

Monday	Tuesday	Wednesday	Thursday	Friday	Saturday	Sunday
				1	2	3
4	5	6	7	8	9	10
11	12	13	14	15	16	17
18	19	20	21	22	23	24
25	26	27	28	29	30	31

AUGUST

Monday	Tuesday	Wednesday	Thursday	Friday	Saturday	Sunday
1	2	3	4	5	6	7
8	9	10	11	12	13	14
15	16	17	18	19	20	21
22	23	24	25	26	27	28
29	30	31				

SEPTEMBER

Monday	Tuesday	Wednesday	Thursday	Friday	Saturday	Sunday
			1	2	3	4
5	6	7	8	9	10	11
12	13	14	15	16	17	18
19	20	21	22	23	24	25
26	27	28	29	30		

OCTOBER

Monday	Tuesday	Wednesday	Thursday	Friday	Saturday	Sunday
					1	2
3	4	5	6	7	8	9
10	11	12	13	14	15	16
17	18	19	20	21	22	23
24	25	26	27	28	29	30

OCTOBER / NOVEMBER

Monday	Tuesday	Wednesday	Thursday	Friday	Saturday	Sunday
31	1	2	3	4	5	6
7	8	9	10	11	12	13
14	15	16	17	18	19	20
21	22	23	24	25	26	27
28	29	30				

DECEMBER

Monday	Tuesday	Wednesday	Thursday	Friday	Saturday	Sunday
			1	2	3	4
5	6	7	8	9	10	11
12	13	14	15	16	17	18
19	20	21	22	23	24	25
26	27	28	29	30	31	

KIM LIM
Red Aquatint 1972
Etching and aquatint on paper
44.5 × 44.5 cm
Tate. Presented by Waddington Galleries through the Institute of Contemporary Prints 1975

DECEMBER / JANUARY

27 Monday

31 Friday

28 Tuesday

1 Saturday

29 Wednesday

2 Sunday

30 Thursday

Monday		3	10	17	24	31
Tuesday		4	11	18	25	
Wednesday		5	12	19	26	
Thursday		6	13	20	27	
Friday		7	14	21	28	
Saturday	1	8	15	22	29	
Sunday	2	9	16	23	30	

WALTER RICHARD SICKERT
Minnie Cunningham at the Old Bedford 1892
Oil paint on canvas
76.5 × 63.8 cm
Tate. Purchased 1976

JANUARY

3 Monday

4 Tuesday

5 Wednesday

6 Thursday

7 Friday

8 Saturday

9 Sunday

Monday		3	10	17	24	31
Tuesday		4	11	18	25	
Wednesday		5	12	19	26	
Thursday		6	13	20	27	
Friday		7	14	21	28	
Saturday	1	8	15	22	29	
Sunday	2	9	16	23	30	

MENASHE KADISHMAN
Cracked Earth B 1979
Screenprint on paper
78.8 × 61 cm
Tate. Presented by Rose and Chris Prater 1979
© Menashe Kadishman, courtesy www.kadishman.com

JANUARY

10 Monday

14 Friday

11 Tuesday

15 Saturday

12 Wednesday

16 Sunday

13 Thursday

Monday		3	10	17	24	31
Tuesday		4	11	18	25
Wednesday		5	12	19	26
Thursday		6	13	20	27
Friday		7	14	21	28
Saturday	1	8	15	22	29
Sunday	2	9	16	23	30

PIET MONDRIAN
Composition B (No.II) with Red 1935
Oil paint on canvas
80.3 × 63.3 × 2.4 cm

Tate. Accepted by HM Government in lieu of tax with additional payment (General Funds) made with assistance from the National Lottery through the Heritage Lottery Fund, the Art Fund, the Friends of the Tate Gallery and the Dr V.J. Daniel Bequest 1999

JANUARY

17 Monday

18 Tuesday

19 Wednesday

20 Thursday

21 Friday

22 Saturday

23 Sunday

Monday		3	10	17	24	31
Tuesday		4	11	18	25
Wednesday		5	12	19	26
Thursday		6	13	20	27
Friday		7	14	21	28
Saturday	1	8	15	22	29
Sunday	2	9	16	23	30

PIERRE BONNARD
Coffee 1915
Oil paint on canvas
73 × 106.4 cm
Tate. Presented by Sir Michael Sadler through the Art Fund 1941

JANUARY

24 Monday

28 Friday

25 Tuesday

29 Saturday

26 Wednesday

30 Sunday

27 Thursday

Monday	3	10	17	24
Tuesday	4	11	18	25
Wednesday	5	12	19	26
Thursday	6	13	20	27
Friday	7	14	21	28
Saturday	1	8	15	22	29
Sunday	2	9	16	23	30

BARBARA HEPWORTH
Three Forms 1969
Lithograph on paper
45.7 × 59.7 cm
Tate. Presented by Curwen Studio through the Institute of Contemporary Prints 1975
Barbara Hepworth © Bowness

JANUARY / FEBRUARY

31 Monday

1 Tuesday

2 Wednesday

3 Thursday

4 Friday

5 Saturday

6 Sunday

Monday		7	14	21	28
Tuesday	1	8	15	22	
Wednesday	2	9	16	23	
Thursday	3	10	17	24	
Friday	4	11	18	25	
Saturday	5	12	19	26	
Sunday	6	13	20	27	

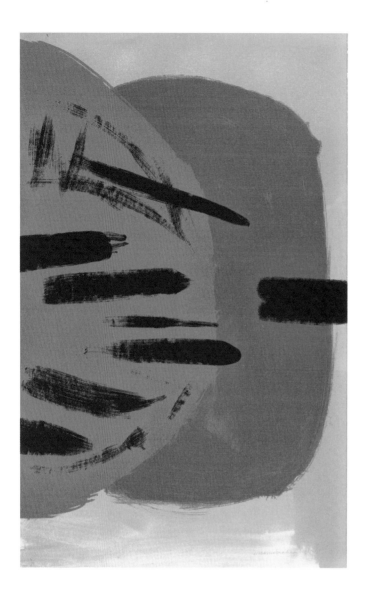

WILHELMINA BARNS-GRAHAM
Orange and Red on Pink 1991
Screenprint on paper
76 × 48.5 cm
Tate. Presented by The Barns-Graham Charitable Trust 2012
© Wilhelmina Barns-Graham Trust

FEBRUARY

7 Monday

11 Friday

8 Tuesday

12 Saturday

9 Wednesday

13 Sunday

10 Thursday

Monday		7	14	21	28
Tuesday	1	8	15	22	
Wednesday	2	9	16	23	
Thursday	3	10	17	24	
Friday	4	11	18	25	
Saturday	5	12	19	26	
Sunday	6	13	20	27	

ROELOF LOUW
Soul City (Pyramid of Oranges) 1967
Oranges, wood, plastic
152.4 × 166.7 × 166.7 cm
Tate. Presented by Tate Patrons 2013
© Roelof Louw

FEBRUARY

14 Monday

18 Friday

15 Tuesday

19 Saturday

16 Wednesday

20 Sunday

17 Thursday

Monday		7	14	21	28
Tuesday	1	8	15	22
Wednesday	2	9	16	23
Thursday	3	10	17	24
Friday	4	11	18	25
Saturday	5	12	19	26
Sunday	6	13	20	27

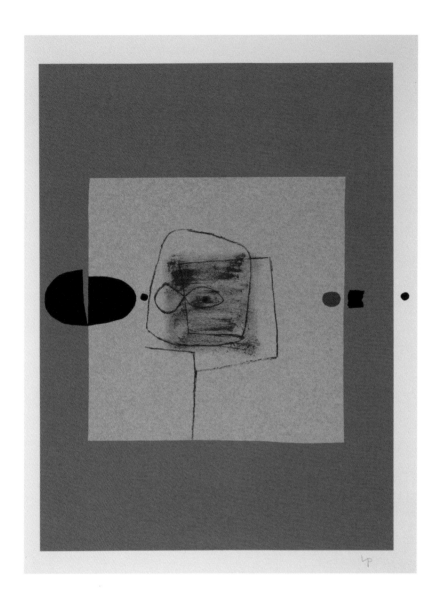

VICTOR PASMORE
Points of Contact No. 27 1974
Screenprint on paper
73.7 × 57.8 cm
Tate. Presented by Rose and Chris Prater through the Institute of Contemporary Prints 1975
© Tate

FEBRUARY

21 Monday

22 Tuesday

23 Wednesday

24 Thursday

25 Friday

26 Saturday

27 Sunday

Monday		7	14	21	28
Tuesday	1	8	15	22
Wednesday	2	9	16	23
Thursday	3	10	17	24
Friday	4	11	18	25
Saturday	5	12	19	26
Sunday	6	13	20	27

DAVID BOMBERG
Trees in Sun, Cyprus 1948
Oil paint on canvas
63.9 × 76.5 cm
Tate. Purchased 1992
© Tate

FEBRUARY / MARCH

28 Monday

1 Tuesday

2 Wednesday

3 Thursday

4 Friday

5 Saturday

6 Sunday

Monday		7	14	21	28
Tuesday	1	8	15	22	29
Wednesday	2	9	16	23	30
Thursday	3	10	17	24	31
Friday	4	11	18	25	
Saturday	5	12	19	26	
Sunday	6	13	20	27	

DANTE GABRIEL ROSSETTI
Woman in Yellow 1863
Watercolour on paper
58.5 × 49.4 × 5 cm
Tate. Bequeathed by Beresford Rimington Heaton 1940

MARCH

7 Monday

8 Tuesday

9 Wednesday

10 Thursday

11 Friday

12 Saturday

13 Sunday

Monday		7	14	21	28
Tuesday	1	8	15	22	29
Wednesday	2	9	16	23	30
Thursday	3	10	17	24	31
Friday	4	11	18	25	
Saturday	5	12	19	26	
Sunday	6	13	20	27	

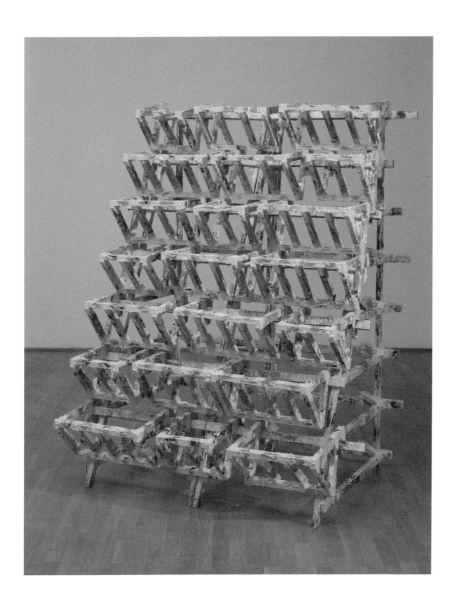

PHYLLIDA BARLOW
Untitled (Yellow Rack) 2006
Timber, galvanised steel and plaster
189 × 155.7 × 116 cm
Tate. Purchased 2007
© Phyllida Barlow

MARCH

14 Monday

15 Tuesday

16 Wednesday

17 Thursday

18 Friday

19 Saturday

20 Sunday

Monday		7	14	21	28
Tuesday	1	8	15	22	29
Wednesday	2	9	16	23	30
Thursday	3	10	17	24	31
Friday	4	11	18	25	
Saturday	5	12	19	26	
Sunday	6	13	20	27	

WASSILY KANDINSKY
Cossacks 1910–11
Oil paint on canvas
94.6 × 130.2 cm
Tate. Presented by Mrs Hazel McKinley 1938

MARCH

21 Monday

22 Tuesday

23 Wednesday

24 Thursday

25 Friday

26 Saturday

27 Sunday

Monday		7	14	21	28
Tuesday	1	8	15	22	29
Wednesday	2	9	16	23	30
Thursday	3	10	17	24	31
Friday	4	11	18	25	
Saturday	5	12	19	26	
Sunday	6	13	20	27	

VANESSA BELL
Interior with a Table 1921
Oil paint on canvas
54 × 64.1 cm
Tate. Bequeathed by Frank Hindley Smith 1940
© Tate

MARCH / APRIL

28 Monday

29 Tuesday

30 Wednesday

31 Thursday

1 Friday

2 Saturday

3 Sunday

Monday		4	11	18	25
Tuesday		5	12	19	26
Wednesday		6	13	20	27
Thursday		7	14	21	28
Friday	1	8	15	22	29
Saturday	2	9	16	23	30
Sunday	3	10	17	24	

ANWAR JALAL SHEMZA
Composition in Red and Green, Squares and Circles 1963
Oil paint on canvas
91.1 × 72 × 1.8 cm
Tate. Purchased with assistance from Tate Patrons 2017

APRIL

4 Monday

5 Tuesday

6 Wednesday

7 Thursday

8 Friday

9 Saturday

10 Sunday

Monday		4	11	18	25
Tuesday		5	12	19	26
Wednesday		6	13	20	27
Thursday		7	14	21	28
Friday	1	8	15	22	29
Saturday	2	9	16	23	30
Sunday	3	10	17	24	

VINCENT VAN GOGH
Farms near Auvers 1890
Oil paint on canvas
50.2 × 100.3 cm
Tate. Bequeathed by C. Frank Stoop 1933

APRIL

11 Monday

15 Friday

12 Tuesday

16 Saturday

13 Wednesday

17 Sunday

14 Thursday

Monday		4	11	18	25
Tuesday		5	12	19	26
Wednesday		6	13	20	27
Thursday		7	14	21	28
Friday	1	8	15	22	29
Saturday	2	9	16	23	30
Sunday	3	10	17	24	

CARMEN HERRERA
Green Garden 1950
Acrylic on canvas
45.5 x 60.8 cm
18 x 24 in
© Carmen Herrera; Courtesy Lisson Gallery

APRIL

18 Monday

19 Tuesday

20 Wednesday

21 Thursday

22 Friday

23 Saturday

24 Sunday

Monday		4	11	18	25
Tuesday		5	12	19	26
Wednesday		6	13	20	27
Thursday		7	14	21	28
Friday	1	8	15	22	29
Saturday	2	9	16	23	30
Sunday	3	10	17	24	

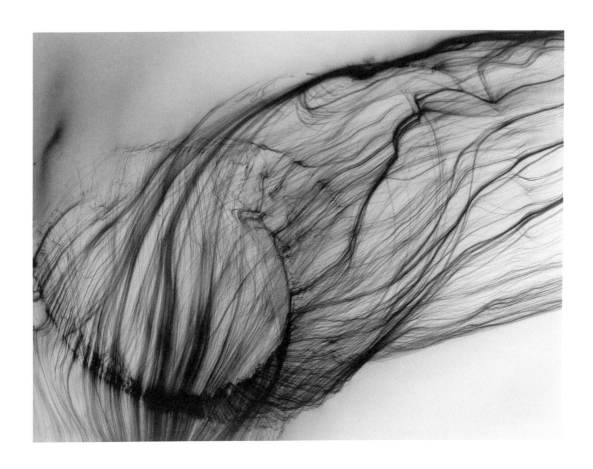

WOLFGANG TILLMANS
Freischwimmer 16 2003
Photograph, c-print on paper
239.5 × 179.7 cm
Tate. Presented by the artist 2005
© Wolfgang Tillmans, courtesy Maureen Paley, London

APRIL / MAY

25 Monday

29 Friday

26 Tuesday

30 Saturday

27 Wednesday

1 Sunday

28 Thursday

Monday	2	9	16	23	30
Tuesday	3	10	17	24	31
Wednesday	4	11	18	25	
Thursday	5	12	19	26	
Friday	6	13	20	27	
Saturday	7	14	21	28	
Sunday	1	8	15	22	29

J.M.W. TURNER
The Blue Rigi, Sunrise 1842
Watercolour on paper
29.7 × 45 cm

Tate. Purchased with assistance from the National Heritage Memorial Fund, the Art Fund (with a contribution from the Wolfson Foundation and including generous support from David and Susan Gradel, and from other members of the public through the Save the Blue Rigi appeal), Tate Members and other donors 2007

MAY

2 Monday

3 Tuesday

4 Wednesday

5 Thursday

6 Friday

7 Saturday

8 Sunday

Monday		2	9	16	23	30
Tuesday		3	10	17	24	31
Wednesday		4	11	18	25
Thursday		5	12	19	26
Friday		6	13	20	27
Saturday		7	14	21	28
Sunday	1	8	15	22	29

RACHEL WHITEREAD
Study (Blue) for 'Floor' 1992
Correction fluid, ink and watercolour on paper
42.5 × 58.5 cm
Tate. Presented anonymously in memory of Adrian Ward-Jackson 1994
© Rachel Whiteread

MAY

9 Monday

13 Friday

10 Tuesday

14 Saturday

11 Wednesday

15 Sunday

12 Thursday

Monday		2	9	16	23	30
Tuesday		3	10	17	24	31
Wednesday		4	11	18	25	
Thursday		5	12	19	26	
Friday		6	13	20	27	
Saturday		7	14	21	28	
Sunday	1	8	15	22	29	

ALFRED WALLIS
'The Hold House Port Mear Square Island Port Mear Beach' c.1932
Oil paint on board
30.5 × 38.7 cm
Tate. Presented by Dame Barbara Hepworth 1968

MAY

16 Monday

17 Tuesday

18 Wednesday

19 Thursday

20 Friday

21 Saturday

22 Sunday

Monday		2	9	16	23	30
Tuesday		3	10	17	24	31
Wednesday		4	11	18	25	
Thursday		5	12	19	26	
Friday		6	13	20	27	
Saturday		7	14	21	28	
Sunday	1	8	15	22	29	

SALOUA RAOUDA CHOUCAIR
Composition in Blue Module 1947–51
Oil paint on canvas
59.5 × 80 cm
Tate. Purchased with funds provided by the Middle East North Africa Acquisitions Committee 2011

MAY

23 Monday

27 Friday

24 Tuesday

28 Saturday

25 Wednesday

29 Sunday

26 Thursday

Monday		2	9	16	23	30
Tuesday		3	10	17	24	31
Wednesday		4	11	18	25	
Thursday		5	12	19	26	
Friday		6	13	20	27	
Saturday		7	14	21	28	
Sunday	1	8	15	22	29	

GLUCK
Flora's Cloak c.1923
Oil paint on canvas
66.4 × 41 cm
Tate. Purchased with funds provided by the Denise Coates Foundation on the occasion of the 2018 centenary of women gaining the right to vote in Britain 2019

MAY / JUNE

30 Monday

3 Friday

31 Tuesday

4 Saturday

1 Wednesday

5 Sunday

2 Thursday

Monday		6	13	20	27
Tuesday		7	14	21	28
Wednesday	1	8	15	22	29
Thursday	2	9	16	23	30
Friday	3	10	17	24	
Saturday	4	11	18	25	
Sunday	5	12	19	26	

MARY FEDDEN
Mauve Still Life 1968
Oil paint on hardboard
61 × 81.9 cm
Tate. Presented by the artist 1997
© The estate of Mary Fedden / Bridgeman Images

JUNE

6 Monday

10 Friday

7 Tuesday

11 Saturday

8 Wednesday

12 Sunday

9 Thursday

Monday		6	13	20	27
Tuesday		7	14	21	28
Wednesday	1	8	15	22	29
Thursday	2	9	16	23	30
Friday	3	10	17	24	
Saturday	4	11	18	25	
Sunday	5	12	19	26	

ROBERT BEVAN
The Cab Horse c.1910
Oil paint on canvas
63.5 × 76.2 cm
Tate. Presented by the Trustees of the Duveen Paintings Fund 1949

JUNE

13 Monday

17 Friday

14 Tuesday

18 Saturday

15 Wednesday

19 Sunday

16 Thursday

Monday		6	13	20	27
Tuesday		7	14	21	28
Wednesday	1	8	15	22	29
Thursday	2	9	16	23	30
Friday	3	10	17	24	
Saturday	4	11	18	25	
Sunday	5	12	19	26	

MORRIS LOUIS
Phi 1960–1
Acrylic paint on canvas
265 × 362 cm
Tate. Bequeathed by Dr Marcella Louis Brenner, the artist's widow 2007, accessioned 2011
© Tate

JUNE

20 Monday

21 Tuesday

22 Wednesday

23 Thursday

24 Friday

25 Saturday

26 Sunday

Monday		6	13	20	27
Tuesday		7	14	21	28
Wednesday	1	8	15	22	29
Thursday	2	9	16	23	30
Friday	3	10	17	24	
Saturday	4	11	18	25	
Sunday	5	12	19	26	

JEAN SPENCER
[no title] 1997
Oil paint on canvas
112.7 × 150.1 × 2.2 cm
Tate. Presented by the artist's family 2000
© Tate

JUNE / JULY

27 Monday

28 Tuesday

29 Wednesday

30 Thursday

1 Friday

2 Saturday

3 Sunday

Monday		4	11	18	25
Tuesday		5	12	19	26
Wednesday		6	13	20	27
Thursday		7	14	21	28
Friday	1	8	15	22	29
Saturday	2	9	16	23	30
Sunday	3	10	17	24	31

NJIDEKA AKUNYILI CROSBY
Predecessors 2013
2 works on paper, charcoal, acrylic paint, graphite and transfer print
212 × 212.3 cm
212 × 212.9 cm
Tate. Purchased with funds provided by the Acquisitions Fund for African Art supported by Guaranty Trust Bank Plc 2014
© Njideka Akunyili Crosby. Photo credit: Jason Wyche (left panel) and Sylvain Deleu (right panel)

JULY

4 Monday

5 Tuesday

6 Wednesday

7 Thursday

8 Friday

9 Saturday

10 Sunday

Monday		4	11	18	25
Tuesday		5	12	19	26
Wednesday		6	13	20	27
Thursday		7	14	21	28
Friday	1	8	15	22	29
Saturday	2	9	16	23	30
Sunday	3	10	17	24	31

HC 9/10   Moore

HENRY MOORE
Seated Figure II: Pink Background 1974
Graphics
Image: 234 x 158 mm
Lithograph in five colours
CGM 408
© Reproduced by permission of The Henry Moore Foundation

JULY

11 Monday

15 Friday

12 Tuesday

16 Saturday

13 Wednesday

17 Sunday

14 Thursday

Monday		4	11	18	25
Tuesday		5	12	19	26
Wednesday		6	13	20	27
Thursday		7	14	21	28
Friday	1	8	15	22	29
Saturday	2	9	16	23	30
Sunday	3	10	17	24	31

JADÉ FADOJUTIMI
I Present Your Royal Highness 2018
Oil paint on canvas
201.5 × 161.1 cm
Tate. Purchased with funds provided by Anders and Yukiko Schroeder 2019
© Jadé Fadojutimi

JULY

18 Monday

22 Friday

19 Tuesday

23 Saturday

20 Wednesday

24 Sunday

21 Thursday

Monday		4	11	18	25
Tuesday		5	12	19	26
Wednesday		6	13	20	27
Thursday		7	14	21	28
Friday	1	8	15	22	29
Saturday	2	9	16	23	30
Sunday	3	10	17	24	31

JOHN SAMUEL RAVEN
Study for 'Saintfoin in Bloom': View near Cobham in Kent 1857
Oil paint on card on wood
17.7 × 35.5 cm
Tate. Presented by the Friends of the Tate Gallery 1981

JULY

25 Monday

26 Tuesday

27 Wednesday

28 Thursday

29 Friday

30 Saturday

31 Sunday

Monday		4	11	18	25
Tuesday		5	12	19	26
Wednesday		6	13	20	27
Thursday		7	14	21	28
Friday	1	8	15	22	29
Saturday	2	9	16	23	30
Sunday	3	10	17	24	31

WILLIAM NICHOLSON
Silver 1938
Oil paint on wood
43.8 × 57.1 cm
Tate. Purchased 1938

AUGUST

1 Monday

2 Tuesday

3 Wednesday

4 Thursday

5 Friday

6 Saturday

7 Sunday

Monday	1	8	15	22	29
Tuesday	2	9	16	23	30
Wednesday	3	10	17	24	31
Thursday	4	11	18	25	
Friday	5	12	19	26	
Saturday	6	13	20	27	
Sunday	7	14	21	28	

JAMES ABBOTT MCNEILL WHISTLER
Nocturne: Blue and Silver - Cremorne Lights 1872
Oil paint on canvas
50.2 × 74.3 cm
Tate. Bequeathed by Arthur Studd 1919

AUGUST

8 Monday

9 Tuesday

10 Wednesday

11 Thursday

12 Friday

13 Saturday

14 Sunday

Monday	1	8	15	22	29
Tuesday	2	9	16	23	30
Wednesday	3	10	17	24	31
Thursday	4	11	18	25	
Friday	5	12	19	26	
Saturday	6	13	20	27	
Sunday	7	14	21	28	

SIRKKA-LIISA KONTTINEN
Girl on a Spacehopper, Byker, 1971
Photograph, gelatin silver print on paper
50.6 × 40.6 cm
Tate. Presented by the artist 2015
© Sirkka-Liisa Konttinen

AUGUST

15 Monday

16 Tuesday

17 Wednesday

18 Thursday

19 Friday

20 Saturday

21 Sunday

Monday	1	8	15	22	29
Tuesday	2	9	16	23	30
Wednesday	3	10	17	24	31
Thursday	4	11	18	25	
Friday	5	12	19	26	
Saturday	6	13	20	27	
Sunday	7	14	21	28	

CORNELIA PARKER
Object That Fell off the White Cliffs of Dover 1992
Silver teapot
12 × 22.5 × 20 cm
Tate. Purchased 1998
© Cornelia Parker

AUGUST

22 Monday

23 Tuesday

24 Wednesday

25 Thursday

26 Friday

27 Saturday

28 Sunday

Monday	1	8	15	22	29
Tuesday	2	9	16	23	30
Wednesday	3	10	17	24	31
Thursday	4	11	18	25	
Friday	5	12	19	26	
Saturday	6	13	20	27	
Sunday	7	14	21	28	

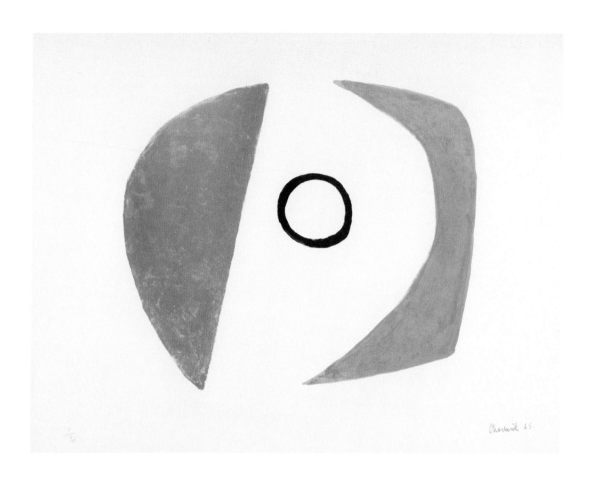

LYNN CHADWICK
Moon Series C 1965–6
Lithograph on paper
50.5 × 65.8 cm
Tate. Presented by Marlborough Graphics through the Institute of Contemporary Prints 1975
© The estate of Lynn Chadwick. All Rights Reserved 2020 / Bridgeman Images

AUGUST / SEPTEMBER

29 Monday

30 Tuesday

31 Wednesday

1 Thursday

2 Friday

3 Saturday

4 Sunday

Monday	5	12	19	26
Tuesday	6	13	20	27
Wednesday	7	14	21	28
Thursday	1	8	15	22	29
Friday	2	9	16	23	30
Saturday	3	10	17	24
Sunday	4	11	18	25

EDGAR DEGAS
Little Dancer Aged Fourteen 1880–1, cast c.1922
Painted bronze with muslin and silk on wooden base
Object: 98.4 × 41.9 × 36.5 cm, 31 kg
Tate. Purchased with assistance from the Art Fund 1952

SEPTEMBER

5 Monday

9 Friday

6 Tuesday

10 Saturday

7 Wednesday

11 Sunday

8 Thursday

Monday		5	12	19	26
Tuesday		6	13	20	27
Wednesday		7	14	21	28
Thursday	1	8	15	22	29
Friday	2	9	16	23	30
Saturday	3	10	17	24	
Sunday	4	11	18	25	

ANNI ALBERS
TR III 1969–70
Screenprint on paper
42 × 47 cm
Tate. Presented by the American Fund for the Tate Gallery, courtesy of Melinda Shearer Maddock 2017
© 2020 The Josef and Anni Albers Foundation/Artists Rights Society (ARS), New York/DACS, London

SEPTEMBER

12 Monday

16 Friday

13 Tuesday

17 Saturday

14 Wednesday

18 Sunday

15 Thursday

Monday		5	12	19	26
Tuesday		6	13	20	27
Wednesday		7	14	21	28
Thursday	1	8	15	22	29
Friday	2	9	16	23	30
Saturday	3	10	17	24	
Sunday	4	11	18	25	

CONSTANTIN BRANCUSI
Danaïde c.1918
Bronze on limestone base
Object: 27.9 × 17.1 × 21 cm (base included), 10kg
Tate. Presented by Sir Charles Clore 1959

SEPTEMBER

19 Monday

23 Friday

20 Tuesday

24 Saturday

21 Wednesday

25 Sunday

22 Thursday

Monday		5	12	19	26
Tuesday		6	13	20	27
Wednesday		7	14	21	28
Thursday	1	8	15	22	29
Friday	2	9	16	23	30
Saturday	3	10	17	24	
Sunday	4	11	18	25	

VIRGINIA CHIHOTA
Kuzvirwisa (Fighting Self) 2016
Screenprint on paper
Unconfirmed: 130 × 180 cm
Tate. Purchased with funds provided by the Guaranty Trust Bank plc 2017
© Virginia Chihota

SEPTEMBER / OCTOBER

26 Monday

27 Tuesday

28 Wednesday

29 Thursday

30 Friday

1 Saturday

2 Sunday

Monday		3	10	17	24	31
Tuesday		4	11	18	25
Wednesday		5	12	19	26
Thursday		6	13	20	27
Friday		7	14	21	28
Saturday	1	8	15	22	29
Sunday	2	9	16	23	30

DOROTHY BOHM
Paris 1970
Photograph, gelatin silver print on paper
24.5 × 19.2 cm
Tate. Accepted by HM Government in lieu of inheritance tax from the Estate of Barbara Lloyd and allocated to Tate 2009
© Dorothy Bohm

OCTOBER

3 Monday

4 Tuesday

5 Wednesday

6 Thursday

7 Friday

8 Saturday

9 Sunday

Monday	3	10	17	24	31
Tuesday	4	11	18	25	
Wednesday	5	12	19	26	
Thursday	6	13	20	27	
Friday	7	14	21	28	
Saturday	1	8	15	22	29
Sunday	2	9	16	23	30

DÓRA MAURER
Seven Foldings 1975, published 1978
Drypoint on paper
57.8 × 40 cm
Tate. Purchased 1985
© Dóra Maurer

OCTOBER

10 Monday

14 Friday

11 Tuesday

15 Saturday

12 Wednesday

16 Sunday

13 Thursday

Monday		3	10	17	24	31
Tuesday		4	11	18	25	
Wednesday		5	12	19	26	
Thursday		6	13	20	27	
Friday		7	14	21	28	
Saturday	1	8	15	22	29	
Sunday	2	9	16	23	30	

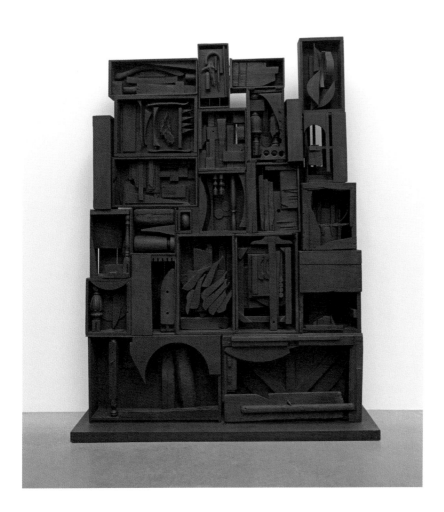

LOUISE NEVELSON
Black Wall 1959
Painted wood
264.2 × 216.5 × 64.8 cm
Tate. Presented by the Friends of the Tate Gallery 1962
© ARS, NY and DACS, London 2020

OCTOBER

17 Monday

21 Friday

18 Tuesday

22 Saturday

19 Wednesday

23 Sunday

20 Thursday

Monday		3	10	17	24	31
Tuesday		4	11	18	25	
Wednesday		5	12	19	26	
Thursday		6	13	20	27	
Friday		7	14	21	28	
Saturday	1	8	15	22	29	
Sunday	2	9	16	23	30	

ROMARE BEARDEN
Pittsburgh Memory 1964
Photograph, gelatin silver print on paper, mounted on fibreboard
126.5 × 158 cm
Tate. Lent by the Tate Americas Foundation 2017. On long term loan

OCTOBER

24 Monday

28 Friday

25 Tuesday

29 Saturday

26 Wednesday

30 Sunday

27 Thursday

Monday		3	10	17	24	31
Tuesday		4	11	18	25	
Wednesday		5	12	19	26	
Thursday		6	13	20	27	
Friday		7	14	21	28	
Saturday	1	8	15	22	29	
Sunday	2	9	16	23	30	

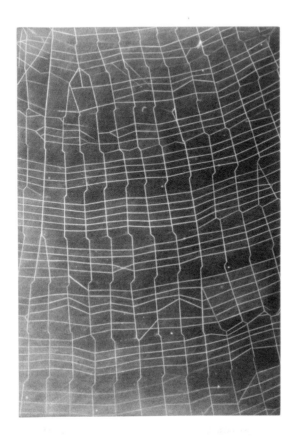

VIJA CELMINS
Web Ladder 2010
Mezzotint on paper
41.7 × 29.9 cm
ARTIST ROOMS Tate and National Galleries of Scotland. Presented by the artist 2011
© Vija Celmins

OCTOBER / NOVEMBER

31 Monday

1 Tuesday

2 Wednesday

3 Thursday

4 Friday

5 Saturday

6 Sunday

Monday		7	14	21	28
Tuesday	1	8	15	22	29
Wednesday	2	9	16	23	30
Thursday	3	10	17	24	
Friday	4	11	18	25	
Saturday	5	12	19	26	
Sunday	6	13	20	27	

LÁSZLÓ MOHOLY-NAGY
K VII 1922
Oil paint and graphite on canvas
115.3 x 135.9 cm
Tate. Purchased 1961

NOVEMBER

7 Monday

11 Friday

8 Tuesday

12 Saturday

9 Wednesday

13 Sunday

10 Thursday

Monday		7	14	21	28
Tuesday	1	8	15	22	29
Wednesday	2	9	16	23	30
Thursday	3	10	17	24	
Friday	4	11	18	25	
Saturday	5	12	19	26	
Sunday	6	13	20	27	

GWEN JOHN
Young Woman Holding a Black Cat c.1920–5
Oil paint on canvas
46 × 29.8 × 1.7 cm
Tate. Purchased 1946

NOVEMBER

14 Monday

18 Friday

15 Tuesday

19 Saturday

16 Wednesday

20 Sunday

17 Thursday

Monday		7	14	21	28
Tuesday	1	8	15	22	29
Wednesday	2	9	16	23	30
Thursday	3	10	17	24	
Friday	4	11	18	25	
Saturday	5	12	19	26	
Sunday	6	13	20	27	

FERNAND LÉGER
Mechanical Elements 1926
Watercolour, graphite and ink on paper
24.2 × 30.3 cm
Tate. Presented by Gustav and Elly Kahnweiler 1974, accessioned 1994
© ADAGP, Paris and DACS, London 2020

NOVEMBER

21 Monday

25 Friday

22 Tuesday

26 Saturday

23 Wednesday

27 Sunday

24 Thursday

Monday		7	14	21	28
Tuesday	1	8	15	22	29
Wednesday	2	9	16	23	30
Thursday	3	10	17	24	
Friday	4	11	18	25	
Saturday	5	12	19	26	
Sunday	6	13	20	27	

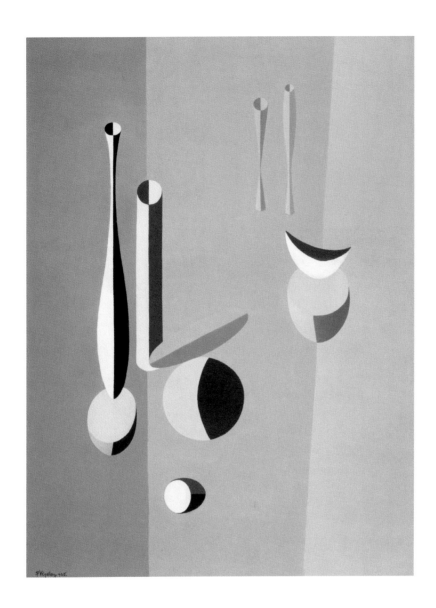

PAULE VÉZELAY
Forms on Grey 1935
Oil paint on canvas
129.9 × 97.1 cm
Tate. Bequeathed by the artist 1985
© The estate of Paule Vézelay

NOVEMBER / DECEMBER

28 Monday

2 Friday

29 Tuesday

3 Saturday

30 Wednesday

4 Sunday

1 Thursday

Monday	5	12	19	26
Tuesday	6	13	20	27
Wednesday	7	14	21	28
Thursday	1	8	15	22	29
Friday	2	9	16	23	30
Saturday	3	10	17	24	31
Sunday	4	11	18	25

ANYA GALLACCIO
White Ice 2002
Screenprint on acrylic
61.5 × 85.5 cm
Tate. Purchased 2004
© Anya Gallaccio, courtesy Lehmann Maupin Gallery, New York

DECEMBER

5 Monday

6 Tuesday

7 Wednesday

8 Thursday

9 Friday

10 Saturday

11 Sunday

Monday		5	12	19	26
Tuesday		6	13	20	27
Wednesday		7	14	21	28
Thursday	1	8	15	22	29
Friday	2	9	16	23	30
Saturday	3	10	17	24	31
Sunday	4	11	18	25	

A.P.   david hockney 66

David Hockney
"In the Dull Village" from *"Illustrations for Fourteen Poems from C.P. Cavafy"* 1966–1967
Etching
Editioned
22 1/2 x 15 1/2"
© David Hockney

DECEMBER

12 Monday

16 Friday

13 Tuesday

17 Saturday

14 Wednesday

18 Sunday

15 Thursday

Monday	5	12	19	26
Tuesday	6	13	20	27
Wednesday	7	14	21	28
Thursday	1	8	15	22	29
Friday	2	9	16	23	30
Saturday	3	10	17	24	31
Sunday	4	11	18	25

MARIE-LOUISE VON MOTESICZKY
Photograph of snow covered trees and garden in Chesterford Gardens, Hampstead [c.1960]–1996
Photograph, black and white film
9 x 9 cm
Tate Archive. Presented by the Trustees of the Marie-Louise von Motesiczky Trust, March 2012
© Marie-Louise von Motesiczky Charitable Trust

DECEMBER

19 Monday

20 Tuesday

21 Wednesday

22 Thursday

23 Friday

24 Saturday

25 Sunday

Monday		5	12	19	26
Tuesday		6	13	20	27
Wednesday		7	14	21	28
Thursday	1	8	15	22	29
Friday	2	9	16	23	30
Saturday	3	10	17	24	31
Sunday	4	11	18	25	

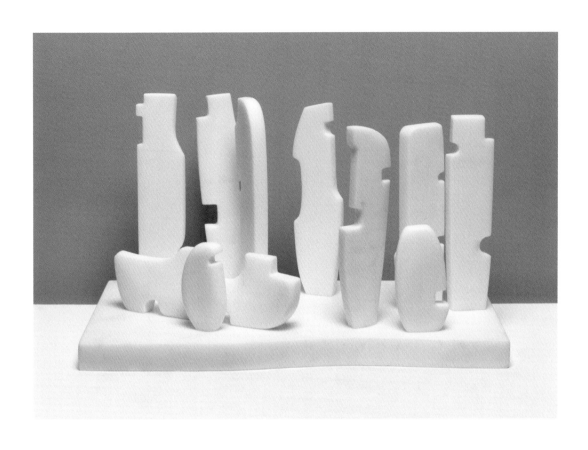

BARBARA HEPWORTH
Group II (People Waiting) 1952
Serravazza marble
Object: 25.5 × 50.7 × 29 cm
Tate. Lent from a private collection 2005
Barbara Hepworth © Bowness

DECEMBER / JANUARY

26 Monday

30 Friday

27 Tuesday

31 Saturday

28 Wednesday

1 Sunday

29 Thursday

Monday		5	12	19	26
Tuesday		6	13	20	27
Wednesday		7	14	21	28
Thursday	1	8	15	22	29
Friday	2	9	16	23	30
Saturday	3	10	17	24	31
Sunday	4	11	18	25	

NAMES AND ADDRESSES

Name:		Name:	
Address		Address	
Home Phone		Home Phone	
Mobile		Mobile	
Email		Email	
Name:		Name:	
Address		Address	
Home Phone		Home Phone	
Mobile		Mobile	
Email		Email	
Name:		Name:	
Address		Address	
Home Phone		Home Phone	
Mobile		Mobile	
Email		Email	

NAMES AND ADDRESSES

Name:		Name:	
Address		Address	
Home Phone		Home Phone	
Mobile		Mobile	
Email		Email	
Name:		Name:	
Address		Address	
Home Phone		Home Phone	
Mobile		Mobile	
Email		Email	
Name:		Name:	
Address		Address	
Home Phone		Home Phone	
Mobile		Mobile	
Email		Email	

NAMES AND ADDRESSES

Name:		Name:	
Address		Address	
Home Phone		Home Phone	
Mobile		Mobile	
Email		Email	
Name:		Name:	
Address		Address	
Home Phone		Home Phone	
Mobile		Mobile	
Email		Email	
Name:		Name:	
Address		Address	
Home Phone		Home Phone	
Mobile		Mobile	
Email		Email	

NAMES AND ADDRESSES

Name:		Name:	
Address		Address	
Home Phone		Home Phone	
Mobile		Mobile	
Email		Email	
Name:		Name:	
Address		Address	
Home Phone		Home Phone	
Mobile		Mobile	
Email		Email	
Name:		Name:	
Address		Address	
Home Phone		Home Phone	
Mobile		Mobile	
Email		Email	

NAMES AND ADDRESSES

Name:		Name:	
Address		Address	
Home Phone		Home Phone	
Mobile		Mobile	
Email		Email	
Name:		Name:	
Address		Address	
Home Phone		Home Phone	
Mobile		Mobile	
Email		Email	
Name:		Name:	
Address		Address	
Home Phone		Home Phone	
Mobile		Mobile	
Email		Email	

NAMES AND ADDRESSES

Name:		Name:	
Address		Address	
Home Phone		Home Phone	
Mobile		Mobile	
Email		Email	
Name:		Name:	
Address		Address	
Home Phone		Home Phone	
Mobile		Mobile	
Email		Email	
Name:		Name:	
Address		Address	
Home Phone		Home Phone	
Mobile		Mobile	
Email		Email	

NAMES AND ADDRESSES

Name:		Name:	
Address		Address	
Home Phone		Home Phone	
Mobile		Mobile	
Email		Email	
Name:		Name:	
Address		Address	
Home Phone		Home Phone	
Mobile		Mobile	
Email		Email	
Name:		Name:	
Address		Address	
Home Phone		Home Phone	
Mobile		Mobile	
Email		Email	

NAMES AND ADDRESSES

Name:		Name:	
Address		Address	
Home Phone		Home Phone	
Mobile		Mobile	
Email		Email	
Name:		Name:	
Address		Address	
Home Phone		Home Phone	
Mobile		Mobile	
Email		Email	
Name:		Name:	
Address		Address	
Home Phone		Home Phone	
Mobile		Mobile	
Email		Email	

NAMES AND ADDRESSES

Name:		Name:	
Address		Address	
Home Phone		Home Phone	
Mobile		Mobile	
Email		Email	
Name:		Name:	
Address		Address	
Home Phone		Home Phone	
Mobile		Mobile	
Email		Email	
Name:		Name:	
Address		Address	
Home Phone		Home Phone	
Mobile		Mobile	
Email		Email	

NAMES AND ADDRESSES

Name:		Name:	
Address		Address	
Home Phone		Home Phone	
Mobile		Mobile	
Email		Email	
Name:		Name:	
Address		Address	
Home Phone		Home Phone	
Mobile		Mobile	
Email		Email	
Name:		Name:	
Address		Address	
Home Phone		Home Phone	
Mobile		Mobile	
Email		Email	

NAMES AND ADDRESSES

Name:		Name:	
Address		Address	
Home Phone		Home Phone	
Mobile		Mobile	
Email		Email	
Name:		Name:	
Address		Address	
Home Phone		Home Phone	
Mobile		Mobile	
Email		Email	
Name:		Name:	
Address		Address	
Home Phone		Home Phone	
Mobile		Mobile	
Email		Email	

NAMES AND ADDRESSES

Name:		Name:	
Address		Address	
Home Phone		Home Phone	
Mobile		Mobile	
Email		Email	
Name:		Name:	
Address		Address	
Home Phone		Home Phone	
Mobile		Mobile	
Email		Email	
Name:		Name:	
Address		Address	
Home Phone		Home Phone	
Mobile		Mobile	
Email		Email	

NOTES

NOTES

NOTES

NOTES

NOTES

NOTES

NOTES

NOTES

PRINCIPAL REGIONAL GALLERIES

ENGLAND

Bedford
The Higgins Bedford
Castle Lane, Bedford MK40 3XD
T: 0123 4718 618
www.thehigginsbedford.org.uk

Birmingham
The Barber Institute of Fine Arts
University of Birmingham
Edgbaston, Birmingham
B15 2TS
T: 0121 414 7333
www.barber.org.uk
Birmingham Museum and Art Gallery
Chamberlain Square
Birmingham B3 3DH
T: 0121 348 8000
www.bmag.org.uk
Ikon Gallery
1 Oozells Square
Birmingham B1 2HS
T: 0121 248 0708
www.ikon-gallery.org

Bolton
Bolton Museum Art Gallery and Aquarium
Le Mans Crescent
Bolton BL1 1SE
T: 01204 332 211
www.boltonlams.co.uk

Bradford
Cartwright Hall Art Gallery
Lister Park, Bradford BD9 4NS
T: 01274 431 212
www.bradfordmuseums.org

Brighton
Brighton Museum and Art Gallery
Royal Pavilion Gardens
Brighton, E Sussex BN1 1EE
T: 0300 029 0900
www.brightonmuseums.org.uk

Bristol
Arnolfini
16 Narrow Quay, Bristol
BS1 4QA
T: 0117 917 2300
www.arnolfini.org.uk

Bristol Museum & Art Gallery
Queen's Road, Bristol BS8 1RL
T: 0117 922 3571
www.bristolmuseums.org.uk

Cambridge
Fitzwilliam Museum
Trumpington Street,
Cambridge CB2 1RB
T: 01223 332 900
www.fitzmuseum.cam.ac.uk
Kettle's Yard
Castle Street, Cambridge
CB3 0AQ
T: 01223 748 100
www.kettlesyard.co.uk

Compton
Watts Gallery
Down Lane, Compton
Guildford, Surrey GU3 1DQ
T: 01483 810235
www.wattsgallery.org.uk

Compton Verney
Compton Verney House
Warwickshire CV35 9HZ
T: 01926 645 500
www.comptonverney.org.uk

Cookham-on-Thames
Stanley Spencer Gallery
High Street Cookham, Berkshire
SL6 9SJ
T: 01628 531 092
www.stanleyspencer.org.uk

Gateshead
BALTIC Centre for Contemporary Art
Gateshead Quays
South Shore Road
Gateshead NE8 3BA
T: 0191 478 1810
www.baltic.art

Shipley Art Gallery
Prince Consort Road
Gateshead NE8 4JB
T: 0191 477 1495
www.shipleyartgallery.co.uk

Hull
Ferens Art Gallery
Little Queen Street
Hull HU1 3RA
T: 01482 300300
www.hcandl.co.uk/museums
-and-galleries/ferens

Ipswich
Christchurch Mansion
Christchurch Park
Soane Street, Ipswich
Suffolk IP4 2BE
T: 01473 433 554
ipswich.cimuseums.org.uk/
visit/christchurch-
mansion/

Kendal
Abbot Hall Art Gallery
Kirkland, Kendal, Cumbria
LA9 5AL
T: 01539 722 464
lakelandarts.org.uk/abbot-hall/

Leeds
Henry Moore Institute
74 The Headrow, Leeds LS1
3AH
T: 0113 378 5350
www.henry-moore.org/hmi
Leeds City Art Gallery
The Headrow, Leeds LS1 3AA
T: 0113 247 8256
www.leeds.gov.uk/artgallery

Liverpool
Lady Lever Art Gallery
Port Sunlight Village
Wirral CH62 5EQ
T: 0151 478 4136
www.liverpoolmuseums.
uk/ladylever
Sudley House
Mossley Hill Road, Aigburth
Liverpool L18 8BX
T: 0151 478 4016
www.liverpoolmuseums.org.
uk/sudley
Tate Liverpool
Albert Dock, Liverpool L3 4BB

T: 0151 702 7400
www.tate.org.uk/liverpool
Walker Art Gallery
William Brown Street
Liverpool L3 8EL
T: 0151 478 4199
www.liverpoolmuseums.org.
uk/walker

Manchester
HOME
2 Tony Wilson Place
Manchester M15 4FN
T: 0161 228 7621
www.homemcr.org/about/
history/cornerhouse
Imperial War Museum North
The Quays, Trafford Wharf
Trafford Park
Manchester M17 1TZ
T: 0161 836 4000
www.iwm.org.uk/north
Manchester Art Gallery
Mosley Street
Manchester M2 3JL
T: 0161 235 8888
www.manchestergalleries.org
The Whitworth Art Gallery
The University of Manchester
Oxford Road
Manchester M15 6ER
T: 0161 275 7450
www.whitworth.manchester.
ac.uk

Margate
Turner Contemporary
The Rendezvous
Margate, Kent CT9 1HG
T: 01843 233 000
www.turnercontemporary.org

Milton Keynes
Milton Keynes Gallery
900 Midsummer Boulevard
Central Milton Keynes MK9 3QA
T: 01908 676 900
www.mkgallery.org

Much Hadham
The Henry Moore Foundation
Dane Tree House, Perry Green
Much Hadham
Hertfordshire SG10 6EE
T: 01279 843 333
www.henry-moore.org/visit/
henry-moore-studios-gardens

Newcastle upon Tyne
Laing Art Gallery
New Bridge Street West
Newcastle upon Tyne NE1 8AG
T: 0191 278 1611
www.laingartgallery.org.uk

Norwich
Norwich Castle Museum and
Art Gallery
Castle Hill, Norwich NR1 3JU
T: 01603 493 625
www.museums.norfolk.gov.uk
Sainsbury Centre for Visual Arts
University of East Anglia
Norwich NR4 7TJ
T: 01603 593 199
www.sainsburycentre.ac.uk

Oxford
Ashmolean Museum
Beaumont Street, Oxford
OX1 2PH
T: 01865 278 000
www.ashmolean.org
Modern Art Oxford
30 Pembroke Street
Oxford OX1 1BP
T: 01865 722 733
www.modernartoxford.org.uk

St Ives
Barbara Hepworth Museum &
Sculpture Garden
Barnoon Hill, St Ives
Cornwall TR26 1AD
T: 01736 796 226
www.tate.org.uk/visit/tate-st-
ives/barbara-hepworth-
museum-and-sculpture-garden
Tate St Ives
Porthmeor Beach, St Ives
Cornwall TR26 1TG
T: 01736 796 226
www.tate.org.uk/stives

Salford
The Lowry
Pier 8, Salford Quays
Greater Manchester M50 3AZ
T: 0843 208 6000
www.thelowry.com
Salford Museum and Art Gallery
Peel Park, The Crescent, Salford
Greater Manchester M5 4WU
T: 0161 778 0800
www.salfordmuseum.com

Salisbury
New Art Centre
Roche Court, East Winterslow
Salisbury, Wiltshire SP5 1BG
T: 01980 862244
www.sculpture.uk.com

Sheffield
Graves Art Gallery
Surrey Street, Sheffield
South Yorkshire S1 2LH
T: 0114 278 2600
www.museums-sheffield.
org.uk
Millennium Galleries
48 Arundel Gate, Sheffield
S1 2PP
T: 0114 278 2600
www.museums-sheffield.
org.uk
Weston Park Museum
Weston Park, Sheffield S10 2TP
T: 0114 278 2600
www.museums-sheffield.
org.uk

Southampton
Southampton City Art Gallery
Civic Centre, Commercial Road
Southampton SO14 7LP
T: 023 8083 4536
www.southamptoncityart
gallery.com

Sudbury
Gainsborough's House
46 Gainsborough Street
Sudbury, Suffolk CO10 2EU
T: 01787 372 958
www.gainsborough.org

Wakefield
The Hepworth Wakefield
Gallery Walk
Wakefield WF1 5AW
T: 01924 247 360
www.hepworthwakefield.org
Yorkshire Sculpture Park
West Bretton
Wakefield WF4 4LG
T: 01924 832 631
www.ysp.org.uk

Walsall
New Art Gallery Walsall
Gallery Square, Walsall
WS2 8LG
T: 01922 654 400
www.thenewartgallerywalsall.
org.uk

York
York Art Gallery
Exhibition Square, York
YO1 7EW
T: 01904 687 687
www.yorkartgallery.org.uk

NORTHERN IRELAND

Belfast
Ulster Museum
Botanic Gardens
Belfast
BT9 5AB
T: 028 9044 0000
www.ulstermuseum.org.uk

SCOTLAND

Aberdeen
Aberdeen Art Gallery
Schoolhill, Aberdeen AB10 1FQ
T: 0300 020 0293
www.aberdeencity.gov.uk/
aagm

Dundee
Dundee Contemporary Arts
152 Nethergate
Dundee DD1 4DY
T: 01382 909 900
www.dca.org.uk
V&A Dundee
1 Riverside Esplanade
Dundee DD1 4EZ
T: 01382 411 611
www.vam.ac.uk/dundee

Edinburgh
City Art Centre
2 Market Street
Edinburgh EH1 1DE
T: 0131 529 3993
www.edinburghmuseums.
org.uk
The Fruitmarket Gallery
45 Market Street
Edinburgh EH1 1DF
T: 0131 225 2383
www.fruitmarket.co.uk
National Gallery of Scotland
The Mound
Edinburgh EH2 2EL
T: 0131 624 6200
www.nationalgalleries.org

Scottish National Gallery of
Modern Art
75 Belford Road
Edinburgh EH4 3DR
T: 0131 624 6200
www.nationalgalleries.org
Scottish National Portrait
Gallery
1 Queen Street
Edinburgh EH2 1JD
T: 0131 624 6200
www.nationalgalleries.org

Glasgow
Burrell Collection
Pollok Country Park
2060 Pollokshaws Road
Glasgow
G43 1AT
T: 0141 287 2550
www.glasgowlife.org.uk
Centre for Contemporary Art
350 Sauchiehall Street
Glasgow G2 3JD
T: 0141 352 4900
www.cca-glasgow.com
Gallery of Modern Art
Royal Exchange Square
Glasgow G1 3AH
T: 0141 287 3050
www.glasgowlife.org.uk

WALES

Cardiff
National Museum Cardiff
Cathays Park, Cardiff CF10 3NP
T: 0300 111 2333
www.museum.wales/cardiff

Swansea
Glynn Vivian Art Gallery
Alexandra Road
Swansea SA1 5DZ
T: 01792 516 900
www.glynnvivian.co.uk

LONDON MUSEUMS AND GALLERIES

Barbican Art Gallery
Barbican Centre, Silk Street
London EC2Y 8DS
T: 020 7638 4141
www.barbican.org.uk

The British Library
96 Euston Road
London NW1 2DB
T: 0330 333 1144
www.bl.uk

The British Museum
Great Russell Street
London WC1B 3DG
T: 020 7323 8000
www.britishmuseum.org

Camden Art Centre
Arkwright Road
London NW3 6DG
T: 020 7472 5500
www.camdenartcentre.org

Churchill Museum &
Cabinet War Rooms
Clive Steps
King Charles Street
London SW1A 2AQ
T: 020 7416 5000
www.iwm.org.uk/visits/
churchill-war-rooms

The Courtauld Institute of Art
Somerset House, Strand
London WC2R 0RN
T: 020 3947 7777
www.courtauld.ac.uk

Crafts Council
44a Pentonville Road
London N1 9BY
T: 020 7806 2500
www.craftscouncil.org.uk

Design Museum
224–238 Kensington High
Street
London W8 6AG
T: 020 3862 5900
www.designmuseum.org

Dulwich Picture Gallery
Gallery Road, Dulwich
London SE21 7AD
T: 020 8693 5254
www.dulwichpicturegallery.
org.uk

Hayward Gallery
Southbank Centre
Belvedere Road
London SE1 8XX
T: 020 3879 9555
www.southbankcentre.co.uk/
venues/hayward-gallery

Hogarth's House
Hogarth Lane
Great West Road, Chiswick
London W4 2QN
T: 020 8994 6757
www.williamhogarthtrust.
org.uk

Horniman Museum
100 London Road, Forest Hill
London SE23 3PQ
T: 020 8699 1872
www.horniman.ac.uk

Hunterian Museum
(temporary closure until 2023)
35–43 Lincoln's Inn Fields
London WC2A 3PE
T: 020 7405 3474
www.rcseng.ac.uk/museums/
hunterian

Imperial War Museum
Lambeth Road
London SE1 6HZ
T: 020 7416 5000
www.iwm.org.uk

Institute of
Contemporary Arts
The Mall
London SW1Y 5AH
T: 020 7930 3647
www.ica.art

Jewish Museum
Raymond Burton House
129–131 Albert Street
London NW1 7NB
T: 020 7284 7384
www.jewishmuseum.org.uk

Kensington Palace
Kensington Gardens
London W8 4PX
T: 020 3166 6000
www.hrp.org.uk

Kenwood House
Hampstead Lane
London NW3 7JR
T: 0370 333 1181
www.english-heritage.org.uk

Leighton House Museum
12 Holland Park Road
London W14 8LZ
T: 020 7602 3316
www.rbkc.gov.uk/
leightonhousemuseums

London Transport Museum
Covent Garden Piazza
London WC2E 7BB
T: 0343 222 5000
www.ltmuseum.co.uk

Museum of the Home
Geffrye Almshouses
136 Kingsland Road
London E2 8EA
T: 020 7739 9893
www.museumofthehome.org.uk

Museum of London
150 London Wall
London EC2Y 5HN
T: 020 7001 9844
www.museumoflondon.org.uk

The National Archives
Bessant Dr, Kew, Richmond
TW9 4DU
T: 020 8876 3444
www.nationalarchives.gov.uk

The National Gallery
Trafalgar Square
London WC2N 5DN
T: 020 7747 2885
www.nationalgallery.org.uk

Natural History Museum
Cromwell Road
London SW7 5BD
T: 020 7942 5000
www.nhm.ac.uk

National Maritime Museum
Park Row, East Greenwich
London SE10 9NF
T: 020 8858 4422
www.rmg.co.uk

National Portrait Gallery
(temporary closure until 2023)
St Martin's Place
London WC2H 0HE
T: 020 7306 0055
www.npg.org.uk

Petrie Museum of Egyptian
Archaeology
University College London
Malet Place
Gower Street
London WC1E 6BT
T: 020 3108 9000
www.ucl.ac.uk/culture/
petrie-museum

The Photographers' Gallery
16–18 Ramillies Street
W1F 7LW
T: 020 7087 9300
www.thephotographersgallery.
org.uk

The Queen's Gallery
Buckingham Palace
London SW1A 1AA
T: 0303 123 7301
https://www.rct.uk/visit/
the-queens-gallery-
buckingham-palace

Royal Academy of Arts
Burlington House
Piccadilly
London W1J 0BD
T: 020 7300 8000
www.royalacademy.org.uk

Royal Armouries
HM Tower of London
London EC3N 4AB
T: 020 3166 6660
www.royalarmouries.org

Royal College of Art
Kensington Gore
London SW7 2EU
T: 020 7590 4444
www.rca.ac.uk

Saatchi Gallery
Duke of York's Headquarters
Kings Road
London SW3 4RY
T: 020 7811 3070
www.saatchigallery.com

Science Museum
Exhibition Road
South Kensington
London SW7 2DD
T: 0800 047 8124
www.sciencemuseum.org.uk

Serpentine Gallery
Kensington Gardens
London W2 3XA
T: 020 7402 6075
www.serpentinegalleries.org

Serpentine North Gallery
West Carriage Drive
London W2 2AR
T: 020 7402 6075
www.serpentinegalleries.org

Sir John Soane's Museum
13 Lincoln's Inn Fields
London WC2A 3BP
T: 020 7405 2107
www.soane.org

Tate Britain
Millbank
London SW1P 4RG
T: 020 7887 8888
www.tate.org.uk/britain

Tate Modern
Bankside
London SE1 9TG
T: 020 7887 8888
www.tate.org.uk/modern

Victoria and Albert Museum
Cromwell Road
London SW7 2RL
T: 020 7942 2000
www.vam.ac.uk

V&A Museum of Childhood
(temporary closure until 2022)
Cambridge Heath Road
London E2 9PA
T: 020 8983 5200
www.museumofchildhood.
org.uk

Wallace Collection
Hertford House
Manchester Square
London W1U 3BN
T: 020 7563 9500
www.wallacecollection.org

Wellcome Collection
183 Euston Rd
London NW1 2BE
T: 020 7611 2222
www.wellcomecollection.org

Whitechapel Gallery
77–82 Whitechapel High Street
London E1 7QX
T: 020 7522 7888
www.whitechapelgallery.org

William Morris Gallery
Lloyd Park
Forest Road, Walthamstow
London E17 4PP
T: 020 8496 4390
www.wmgallery.org.uk

SUPPORTING TATE

Tate relies on a large number of supporters – individuals, foundations, companies and public sector sources – to enable us to deliver our world-class programme of activities. This support is essential for us to be able to acquire works of art for the collection, run education, outreach and exhibition programmes, care for the collection and enable art to be displayed, both digitally and physically, inside and outside Tate.

Your donation will make a real difference to our work and enable others to enjoy Tate and its collection both now and in the future. There are a variety of ways in which you can help support Tate.

TATE PATRONS
Tate Patrons share a strong enthusiasm for art and are committed to giving financial support to Tate on an annual basis. Support from Patrons provides much needed funding for acquisitions, exhibitions, conservation and education projects, which are at the heart of Tate endeavours. By continuing to give every year, Patrons become closely engaged in the life of Tate and are able to share their interest in art in an enjoyable and stimulating environment.

CORPORATE MEMBERSHIP
Corporate Membership at Tate Britain, Tate Liverpool and Tate Modern offers companies opportunities for corporate entertaining and the chance for a wide variety of employee benefits. These include special private views, special access to paying exhibitions, out-of-hours visits and tours, invitations to VIP events and talks at Members' offices.

CORPORATE INVESTMENT
Tate has developed a number of imaginative partnerships with the corporate sector, ranging from international interpretation and exhibition programmes to local outreach and staff development programmes. We are particularly known for our high-profile business marketing initiatives and employee benefit packages.

TATE ANNUAL FUND
A donation to the Annual Fund provides unrestricted support to the gallery, helping to make possible Tate's educational programmes and the care, study and exhibition of our unparalleled collection.

LEGACIES
A legacy can help secure Tate's future and may take the form of a residual share of an estate, a specific cash sum or item of property such as a work of art. Legacies to Tate are free of Inheritance Tax and help to secure a strong future for the collection and galleries.

OFFERS IN LIEU OF TAX
Inheritance Tax can be satisfied by transferring to the government a work of art of outstanding importance. In this case the rate of tax is reduced, and it can be made a condition of the offer that the work of art is allocated to Tate.

GIFTS OF SHARES
All gifts of quoted shares and securities are exempt from Capital Gains Tax. For higher-rate taxpayers, a gift of shares saves Income Tax as well as Capital Gains Tax.

AMERICAN PATRONS OF TATE
American Patrons of Tate is an independent charity based in New York that supports the work of Tate in the United Kingdom. It receives full tax-exempt status from the IRS under section 501 (c) (3), allowing United States taxpayers to receive tax deductions on gifts towards annual membership programs, exhibitions, scholarship and capital projects. For more information please contact the American Patrons of Tate office at American Patrons of Tate, 1285 6th Avenue (35th floor), New York, NY 10019, USA.
Tel: 001 212 882 5119/Fax: 001 212 882 5571.

To support Tate and for further information please contact us at:

Development Office
Tate, Millbank
London SW1P 4RG
Tel: 020 7887 8869/Fax: 020 7887 8098

ISBN: 978-1-84976-778-1
/ 978-1-84976-779-8

Designed by Tate Enterprises Ltd.
Photography by Tate Photography
Published in 2021 by Tate Enterprises Ltd,
Millbank, London SW1P 4RG
www.tate.org.uk/publishing

Printed in China

All holiday dates correct at time of press

Every effort has been made to contact the copyright
holders of the works reproduced. The publishers apologise
for any omissions that may inadvertently have been made.